SCHOLASTIC

Traits
Writing™

Student Handbook

Credits

Cover: © Silman Snozyk / age fotostock; p. 8 b: © Scholastic Inc.; p. 16 t to b: © Tatiana Morozova/Shutterstock, © Blacqbook/Shutterstock, © Pakhnyushcha/Shutterstock, © Jaimie D. Travis/Shutterstock, © Elena Stepanova/ Shutterstock; p. 17 tl: © Tatiana Morozova/Shutterstock, tr: © Pakhnyushcha/Shutterstock, lc: ©Blacqbook/Shutterstock, rc: © Jaimie D. Travis/Shutterstock, bl: © Elena Stepanova/Shutterstock; p. 29: © Rudyanto Wijaya/iStockphoto; p. 35: © DLILLC/Media Bakery; p. 41 tl: © Buzz Buzzer/iStockphoto, br: © Art Vandalay/Getty Images; p. 49: © age fotostock/ SuperStock; p. 55: © MTPA Stock/Masterfile; p. 61 c: © Roy Morsch/Corbis, tr: © David P/iStockphoto; p. 69: © Purdy Photography/iStockphoto; p. 75: © P. Parviainen/Photo Researchers, Inc.; p. 81 l: © iofoto /Shutterstock, r: © Big Cheese Photo/Media Bakery; p. 89 tl: © Sean Justice/Corbis, r: ©Ariel Skelley/Blend Images, b: © Peter Hince/Getty Images; p. 95: © Deco Images/Alamy; p. 101: © Silman Snozyk / age fotostock; p. 109: © Thomas Rodriguez/Corbis; p. 115 c: © Paul A. Souders/Corbis, bl: © Francois Gohier/Photo Researchers, Inc., br: © Paul A. Souders/Corbis; p. 121 l: © Chris Ted/ Getty Images, c: © Paul Simcock/Blend Images/Getty Images, r: © Elke Van de Velde/Getty Images; p. 129 c: © "Sunday Afternoon on the Island of La Grande Jatte," 1884-86 (oil on canvas) by Georges Pierre Seurat (1859-91). The Art Institute of Chicago, IL, USA/The Bridgeman Art Library, bc: © Seth Joel/Getty Images; p. 135: © Glow Images/SuperStock; p. 141: © Greenland /Shutterstock; p. 149: © S. Solum/PhotoLink/Getty Images; p. 155: © Alvis Upitis/Getty Images; p. 161: © Index Stock Imagery/Photolibrary; p. 168 l: © Arvind Balaraman/Shutterstock, c: © Dmitriy Shironosov/Shutterstock, r: © Myrleen Pearson/Alamy; p. 172: © Wealan Pollard /OJO Images/Getty Images; p. 176 cl © PixHook/iStockphoto, b: © Tim UR/Shutterstock

Trait Mates Illustration: Wook Jin Jung

All rights reserved.   Published by Scholastic Inc.   Printed in the U.S.A.

ISBN-13: 978-0-545-35807-1
ISBN-10: 0-545-35807-8

Contents

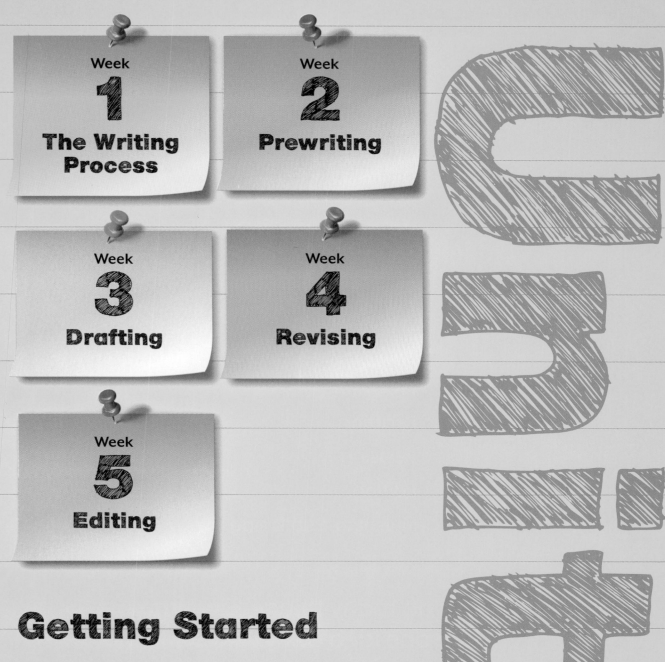

Week 1
The Writing Process

Week 2
Prewriting

Week 3
Drafting

Week 4
Revising

Week 5
Editing

Getting Started

What does a writer do?
How does a writer go from an
idea into a finished piece?
In this unit, you will learn the
answers. Writers love to see
their ideas on a page. You will
too—because you are a writer!

The Writing Process

Prewriting

Drafting

Revising

Editing

Finishing/Publishing

Writers do many things. First, they choose one idea and start drawing and writing. Then, they read their writing over and over, and change some things to make it better. Finally, they share their writing with a reader.

Ready to Write?

- Choose a great idea.
- Get your idea down in words and pictures.
- Change words to make your writing better.
- Watch your spelling and handwriting.

The Writing Process

What Writers Do

What do writers do? Draw and write your ideas here.

The bathtub is ducky!

My Writing Place and "Stuff"

Draw a picture of your favorite place to write.

Draw pictures of things you use to write.

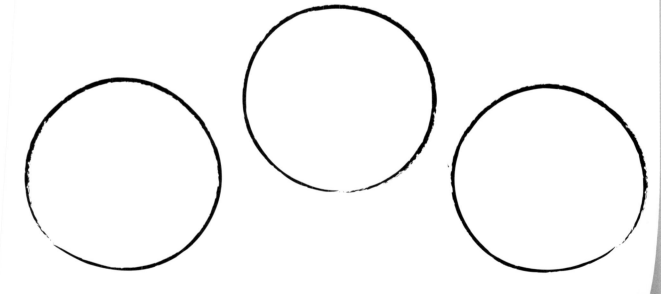

Prewriting

The Writing Process

Prewriting

Drafting

Revising

Editing

Finishing/Publishing

Prewriting is about finding your idea for writing. What do you like to do? Can you tell a story? Do you have a new idea to share? Little things can be big ideas for writing. When you think of an idea, write it down!

I monkey around with karate, too!

Ready to Prewrite?

- Use words and pictures to show ideas.
- Show what you know about the topic.
- Think about what your reader needs to know.
- Find information on your topic.

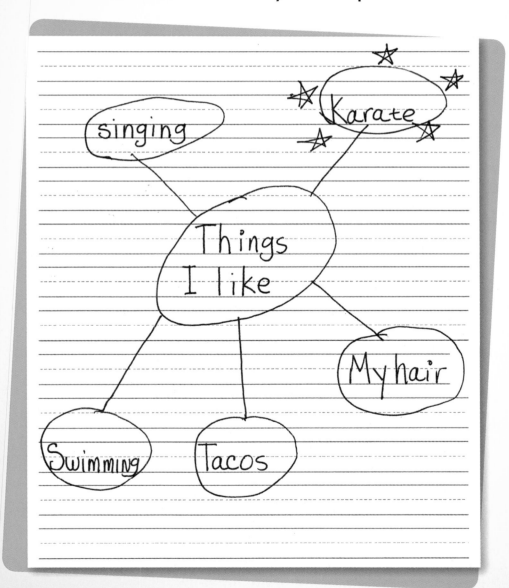

The 5 W's

Imagine a story about your own truck.
Answer the 5 W's below.

1. **What?** _a truck._

   Who? Who is
   driving your truck?

   Why? Why is he or she
   driving your truck?

   When? When does
   the story happen?

   Where? Where does
   the story happen?

2. Write a question about how a truck gets stuck.
   Then answer it.

   Question:

   Answer:

How Trucks Get Stuck

Ask the 5 W's questions about how trucks get stuck.
Write your answers in the circles.

Who?

Where?

What?

a truck

Why?

When?

A stuck truck?
What rotten luck!

Drafting

The Writing Process

Prewriting

Drafting

Revising

Editing

Finishing/Publishing

Drafting is when you get your idea down on paper. You can use words or pictures. The draft is just for you, so don't worry about things like spelling. You can fix them later. Just get your idea down!

Ready to Draft?

- Get your idea down in words and pictures.
- Bring your idea to life.
- Tell the reader about your topic.
- Make the reader want to read more.

I'm takieng karate classes. we did a show for parents and I got to dress up in my gi. ther our boys and girls in my class. The girls our good. we dont even have to wear shoes. My techer is realy nice and shows me what to do

Good start.
Needs more bounce.

Sentence Fluency

Our Senses at the Ocean

Write sense words from *Hello Ocean*.

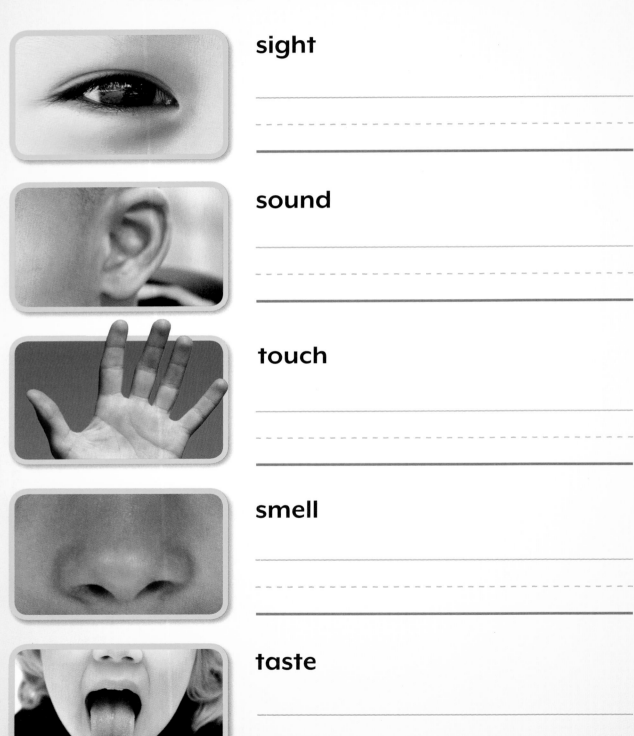

sight

sound

touch

smell

taste

Write about your hometown. Use sense words.

Hello _____

your city or town

sight _____

touch _____

sound _____

smell _____

taste _____

Home is where the "hound" is!

Revising

The Writing Process

Prewriting

Drafting

Revising

Editing

Finishing/Publishing

Revision is how you make your idea as clear and interesting as it can be.

Read over what you wrote.
Should you add some words or pictures?
Should you cut some? Are you saying what you want to say?

Ready to Revise?

- Add things to make your idea clear.
- Take out things that make it fuzzy.
- Make your idea interesting.
- Use words that sound like you.

I love my karate class. I get to dress up in my red gi with a black belt and we don't even wear shoes. When I get better I'll get a new belt to show how much I've learned. ther are boys and girls in my class but I think the girls our better. My techer is so nice. He is call'd a Sensei. The thing I like best about karate is Kicking to use all my strength and let go all my energ Its the best after school. I cant wait to go back again next week

"Gi" whiz, great piece!

Voice

Messy Rooms

What makes Wendell's room messy?
What makes your room messy?

Wendell's Messy Room	**My Room**
1.	1.
2.	2.
3.	3.
4.	4.
5.	5.

Look at the two lists.
Connect items that are the same.

Our Rooms Are a Mess

What makes a room messy?
Write about it here. Then draw a picture.

Tossed toys? Stinky socks? *Rrruff!*

Editing

The Writing Process

Prewriting

Drafting

Revising

Editing

Finishing/Publishing

When you edit, you clean up your writing. Check the spelling. Check for capital letters and punctuation marks. Check your grammar. Make sure your reader understands what you wrote.

Ready to Edit?

- Spell words the best you can.
- Use capital letters and punctuation marks.
- Put spaces between words.
- Make sure the reader can read your writing.

I love my karate class. I get to dress up in my red gi with a black belt and we don't even wear shoes. When I get better I'll get a new belt to show how much I've learned. there are boys and girls in my class but I think the girls our better. My techer is so nice. He is called a Sensei. The thing I like best about karate is kicking to use all my strength and let go all my energy. It's the best after school. I can't wait to go back again next week.

Ready for a black belt in writing!

Presentation

Take Note!

What conventions do you see in *Yo! Yes?* Write them down here.

I Can . . .

Yo! Yes, you can do this!

Conventions

1. Spell *they*.

2. Capitalize *I*.

3. Punctuate my sentence at the end. (**. ! ?**)

4. Put **spaces** between my words.

Week 1 **Ideas**
Finding a Big Idea

Week 2 **Organization**
Starting With a Bold Beginning

Week 3 **Voice**
Expressing a Feeling

Expository Writing Informs or Explains

The writer

- explains something interesting.
- uses facts.
- answers questions.
- focuses on what's important.

Ideas

Focus Mode: Expository

▶ **Finding a Big Idea**

Focusing on the Big Idea

Staying With the Big Idea

Using Juicy Details

Baby birds hatch.

Big ideas do, too.

What helps you hatch a big idea?

Draw it and write about it on the next page.

Finding a Big Idea

What helps you hatch a big idea?
Draw and write about it here.

Our Wildlife Neighbors

What animals did you see on your walk? Write about them.

I saw squirrels. They were nutty!

Writing Sample

Mark this paper's big idea.

Dr. Martin L. King, Jr.
He was born on January 15, 1929.
He brought peace to people.
He was a preacher.
He helped change laws. Blacks could not
drink from the same water fountain
an whites. Black and white people co
uld not go to the same school. He helpe
d changed this. He was killed in
1968.

Ideas

Ideas don't get bigger than this!

My Spelling Words

Write your five spelling words for the week here.

1.

2.

3.

4.

5.

Organization

Focus Mode: Expository

▶ **Starting With
a Bold Beginning**

Creating a Mighty Middle

Finishing With an
Excellent Ending

Adding a Terrific Title

A good piece of writing has a bold beginning.

An elephant has one, too.

What else has a bold beginning?

Draw and write about it on the next page.

Starting With a Bold Beginning

An elephant has a bold beginning. What else has a bold beginning? Draw and write about it here.

Animal Features

Write the animal features you liked in the photos you saw.

> Wow! Those elephants were packing major trunks!

Writing Sample

Mark this paper's bold beginning.

Tommy

Yes! I am a big
sister. I have a baby
brother. His name is
Tommy.
Tommy is a happy boy.
He smiles and laughs at me.
Tommy likes to
play blocks.

Tommy sleeps in the

crib in momys room.
He drinks a bottle.
I like having a baby
brother.

Oh, baby!
That's a bold
beginning!

Organization

Punctuating Powerfully

Add punctuation where it is needed.

1. Birds eat bugs

2. Birds have beaks

3. Why do they have beaks

4. Birds can t read

5. I m a reader

Voice

Focus Mode: Expository

▶ **Expressing a Feeling**

Communicating With Sparkle and Pizzazz

Reaching Out to the Reader

Saying Things in New Ways

A Ferris wheel ride brings out a feeling.

Writing should, too.

What else brings out a feeling?

Draw and write about it on the next page.

Expressing a Feeling

What brings out a feeling in you?
Draw and write about it here.

A Day I Remember

Write about a special day
with friends or family.

I went to the circus.
The clowns "quacked"
me up!

Writing Sample

Mark the feelings in this paper.

I feel sad when my dad has to leave. When my dad has to leave I cry with lonely tears. my face gets wet and I frown. and I yell because I miss my dad so much that I want to stay with him.

I feel bad she feels sad about her dad.

My Spelling Words

Write your five spelling words for the week here.

1. _____

2. _____

3. _____

4. _____

5. _____

Narrative Writing Tells a Story

The writer

- tells an interesting story.

- includes characters.

- sets the story in a time and a place.

- provides a problem and a solution.

Word Choice

Focus Mode: Narrative

▶ **Choosing Zippy Verbs**

Picking "Just Right" Words

Stretching for Never-Before-Tried Words

Using Words to Create Meaning

Word Choice

Good verbs are zippy.

A bicycle can be, too.

What else is zippy?

Draw and write about it on the next page.

Choosing Zippy Verbs

A bicycle can be zippy. What else is zippy?
Draw and write about it here.

My Monster

Give your monster a name. Write zippy verbs to tell how it moves.

My monster likes to shake his monster booty!

My monster's name is _____

He can _____

_____
his eyes.

_____
his ears.

_____
his mouth.

_____
his nose.

_____
his arms.

_____
his feet.

_____
his legs.

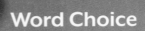
Writing Sample

Mark this paper's zippy verbs.

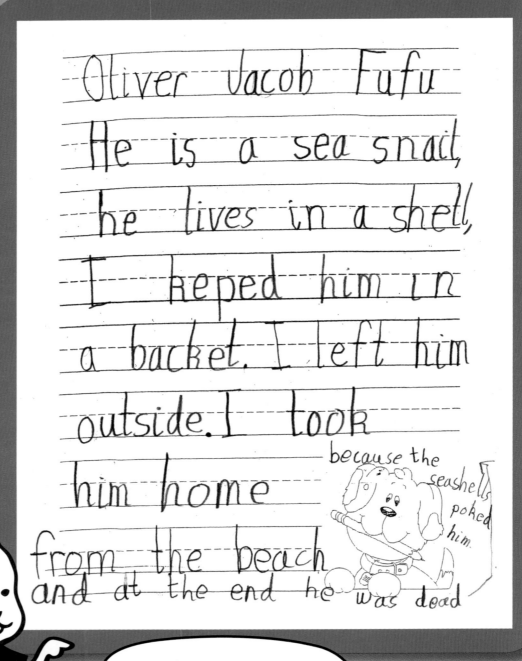

Oliver Jacob Fufu
He is a sea snail,
he lives in a shell,
I keped him in
a backet. I left him
outside. I took
him home *because the seashells poked him*
from the beach
and at the end he was dead

Word Choice

Great piece! This writer *snailed* it!

Capitalizing Correctly

**Circle words that should be capitalized.
Write the correct capital letter.**

1. janita's birthday is february 27.

2. She was born in ohio.

3. Her sister kala was born in florida.

Sentence Fluency

Focus Mode: Narrative

▶ **Building Complete Sentences**

Starting Sentences in Different Ways

Varying Sentence Lengths

Making Smooth-Sounding Sentences

Sentences are carefully built.

Skyscrapers are, too.

What else do you build carefully?

Draw and write about it on the next page.

Building Complete Sentences

What do you build carefully?

Draw and write about it here.

Lost and Found

Write about a lost animal.

> Anyone seen my pal Peter?

Draw a picture of the lost animal.	Where was it found? When?

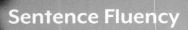

Writing Sample

Mark the complete sentences.

My True Funny Story
When I was little my grandmama
would always kiss me. One Morning
I walked up to her and she gave
me a big kiss. Then all of
a suddan her teeth fell out.
I screamed! I was scerd for a
long time. Now when I missbehav
grandmama takes out her teeth and scers
the bad man out of me.

Talk about telling the "tooth"!

My Spelling Words

Write your five spelling words for the week here.

1.

2.

3.

4.

5.

Ideas

Focus Mode: Narrative

Finding a Big Idea

▶ **Focusing on the Big Idea**

Staying With the Big Idea

Using Juicy Details

Big ideas are better when you see them in focus.

Bugs are cooler when you see them in focus, too.

What else is cool when it is in focus?

Draw and write about it on the next page.

Focusing on the Big Idea

What is cool when it is in focus?
Draw and write about it here.

What If?

Pick an animal and write a
What If? question about it.

If monkeys
could fly, I'd
go bananas!

Draw an animal.	Write a What If? question.

Writing Sample

Mark this paper's big idea.

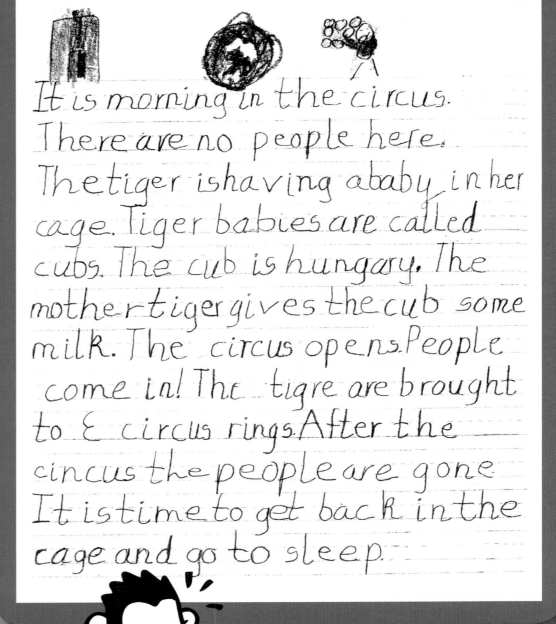

It is morning in the circus. There are no people here. The tiger is having a baby in her cage. Tiger babies are called cubs. The cub is hungary. The mother tiger gives the cub some milk. The circus opens. People come in! The tigre are brought to E circus rings. After the cincus the people are gone. It is time to get back in the cage and go to sleep.

Need a big idea? Try the big top!

Ideas

Applying Basic Grammar

Combine these sentences by using *and* or *but*.
Use a separate piece of paper.

1. The squirrel flew.
   He was not scared.

2. I don't like bees.
   I like spiders.

3. My kit has a net.
   My kit has soap.

4. I can eat grapes.
   I can't eat nuts.

Week 1 Organization
Creating a Mighty Middle

Week 2 Voice
Communicating With Sparkle
and Pizzazz

Week 3 Word Choice
Picking "Just Right" Words

Expository Writing Informs or Explains

The writer

- explains something interesting.

- uses facts.

- answers questions.

- focuses on what's important.

Organization

Focus Mode: Expository

Starting With a
Bold Beginning

▶ **Creating a Mighty Middle**

Finishing With an
Excellent Ending

Adding a Terrific Title

Organization

A camel has a mighty middle.

A good piece of writing has one, too.

What else has a mighty middle?

Draw and write about it on the next page.

Creating a Mighty Middle

What has a mighty middle?
Draw and write about it here.

Things I Like to Do
List three favorite activities.

Barking, eating, and chasing my tail!

1.

2.

3.

Writing Sample

Mark this paper's mighty middle.

I'd like to have dinner with George Washington. He was the first President of United states. We will eat lunch at Olive Garden.

One reason why I want to have dinner with George Washington is because he would teach me how to save the world. We'd pick up trash.

Another reason why I picked him is because he can tell me how it was like to fight in the war. I can ask him if it was hard to fight in the war.

The last reason why I picked him is because he will tell me if he cut down the cherry tree. He cut down his dad's cherry tree with a ax. Haveing dinner with him is going to be very exciting!

By George,
I think he's got it!

My Spelling Words

Write your five spelling words for the week here.

1. _____

2. _____

3. _____

4. _____

5. _____

Voice

Focus Mode: Expository

Expressing a Feeling

▶ **Communicating With Sparkle and Pizzazz**

Reaching Out to the Reader

Saying Things in New Ways

A shooting star has sparkle and pizzazz.

A good piece of writing does, too.

What else has sparkle and pizzazz?

Draw and write about it on the next page.

Communicating With Sparkle and Pizzazz

What has sparkle and pizzazz?
Draw and write about it here.

Animals and Their Babies

List three animals and their babies.
Write something interesting about
each animal.

Make way for this duckling!

Animal	Baby	Something Interesting

Writing Sample

Mark parts of this paper that sparkle.

ANGRY

I felt ANGRY when my frog played dead! Then my mom put him outside for a half hour. Later

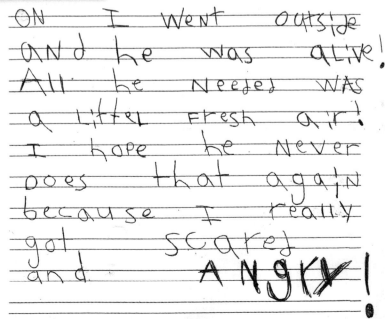

ON I went outside and he was alive! All he needed was a litter fresh air! I hope he never does that again because I really got scared and ANGRY!

Yikes! He's *hoppin'* mad!

Voice

Punctuating Powerfully

Add commas where they are missing.

1. I play with my dog cat and hamster.

2. Lee Tom and I are friends.

3. I drink milk juice and water.

4. I like to paint draw and write.

Word Choice

Focus Mode: Expository

Choosing Zippy Verbs

▶ **Picking "Just Right" Words**

Stretching for
Never-Before-Tried Words

Using Words to
Create Meaning

The paint color of a room should be just right.
The words in your writing should be, too.

What else should be "just right"?
Draw and write about it on the next page.

Picking "Just Right" Words

Think of something that needs to be "just right." Draw and write about it here.

The Right Words to Say Thanks!

Name three things you are thankful for. Write a sentence about them.

I'm thankful for mice, catnip, and kitty litter!

| 1 | 2 | 3 |

Writing Sample

Mark this paper's "just right" words.

This is a fish named wioures. He is
In a ocean. the fish is orange.
He is swimming in the ocean.
He is nice because he is nice tome.
He looks to me wiht round eyes.

Word Choice

Here fishy,
fishy, fishy!

My Spelling Words

Write your five spelling words for the week here.

1. _____

2. _____

3. _____

4. _____

5. _____

Week 1 Sentence Fluency

Starting Sentences in Different Ways

Week 2 Ideas

Staying With the Big Idea

Week 3 Organization

Finishing With an Excellent Ending

Narrative Writing Tells a Story

The writer

- tells an interesting story.

- includes characters.

- sets the story in a time and place.

- provides a problem and solution.

Sentence Fluency

Focus Mode: Narrative

Building Complete Sentences

▶ **Starting Sentences in Different Ways**

Varying Sentence Lengths

Making Smooth-Sounding Sentences

Sentences start in different ways.

Friendships start in different ways, too.

What else starts in different ways?

Draw and write about it on the next page.

Starting Sentences in Different Ways

Friendships start in different ways. What else starts in different ways? Draw and write about it here.

Four Good Friends

Four friends make a plan to do something together. Write what they say to each other.

Ready to write? Hop to it!

1. :

2. :

3. :

4. :

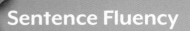

Writing Sample

Mark the beginning of each sentence.
Do the sentences start in different ways?

240!240 legs on a millipede. The millipede made me excited to hold it. Professor Norm got me excited when he said the millipede feels like a walking tooth brush, and it did! Oh I'm telling the truth. It realy tickls!

240 legs? That's a lot of socks!

Sentence Fluency

Capitalizing Correctly

Rewrite the sentences. Use capital letters where they are needed. Use a separate sheet of paper if you need to.

1. i like books.

2. My friend harry likes books, too.

3. We get books on tuesdays in june.

Ideas

Focus Mode: Narrative

Finding a Big Idea

Focusing on the Big Idea

▶ **Staying With the Big Idea**

Using Juicy Details

A boat needs to stay on course.

So does a piece of writing.

What else needs to stay on course?

Draw and write about it on the next page.

Staying With the Big Idea

A sailboat needs to stay on course.
What else needs to stay on course?
Draw and write about it here.

Time to Help

Now that you've read *100th Day Worries*, write about who Jessica will help and how she will help.

I'd like 100 bananas, please.

Who Jessica Will Help	How She Will Help

Writing Sample

Mark this paper's big idea.

chicken pincher
one afternoon I was
down in my chicken pen
feeding the chickens. A
chicken flew right on my
head! He landed
on me and started pinching
my hair! He is the chicken
pincher now.

This chicken went ape!

My Spelling Words

Write your five spelling words for the week here.

1. _____

2. _____

3. _____

4. _____

5. _____

Organization

Focus Mode: Narrative

Starting With a
Bold Beginning

Creating a Mighty Middle

▶ **Finishing With an
Excellent Ending**

Adding a Terrific Title

Organization

A good piece of writing has an excellent ending.

A ride down a waterslide does, too.

What else has an excellent ending?

Draw and write about it on the next page.

Finishing With an Excellent Ending

What else has an excellent ending?
Draw and write about it here.

A Monster Comes to Visit

Write about the monster that comes to visit.

What the Monster Wants	Why the Monster Wants It

Writing Sample

Mark this paper's excellent ending.

oops

One bAY I WAS PLAYIng SOCCer.
i Went To scoreA goAL Anb
feLT something funny. When
I Looked, my PANTS hAb
fALLen bown... bUT I
scoredj

This tale makes me howl!

Applying Basic Grammar

Circle the correct verb in each sentence.

1. Yesterday, the monster (visits, visited) Jeremy.

2. Jeremy (open, opens) the door.

3. The monster (walks, walk) in.

4. Later he (rushed, rush) to the bus stop.

Week 1 Voice

Reaching Out to the Reader

Week 2 Word Choice

Stretching for
Never-Before-Tried Words

Week 3 Sentence
Fluency

Varying Sentence Lengths

**Expository Writing Informs
or Explains**

The writer

- explains something interesting.

- uses facts.

- answers questions.

- focuses on what's important.

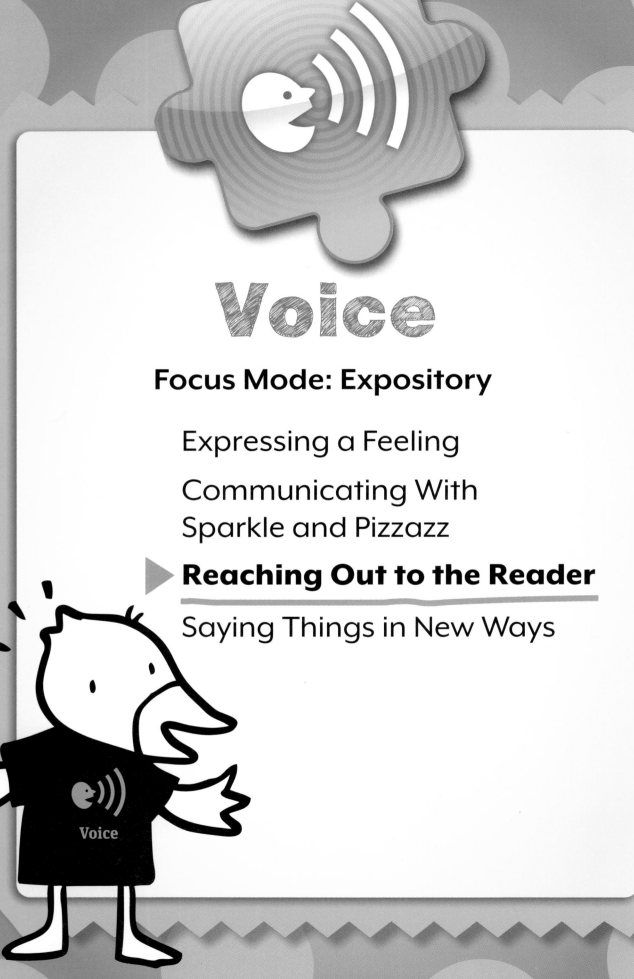

Voice

Focus Mode: Expository

Expressing a Feeling

Communicating With Sparkle and Pizzazz

▶ **Reaching Out to the Reader**

Saying Things in New Ways

Voice

Parents reach out to help their children.

Writers reach out to inform their readers.

Who else reaches out?

Draw and write about that person on the next page.

Reaching Out to the Reader

Can you think of someone else who reaches out? Draw and write about him or her here.

Places at School

List places in the school that visitors might want to find. Then write where they are in the building.

Just waddle this way...

Places in the School	Location

Writing Sample

Mark places where the writer uses voice to reach out to the reader.

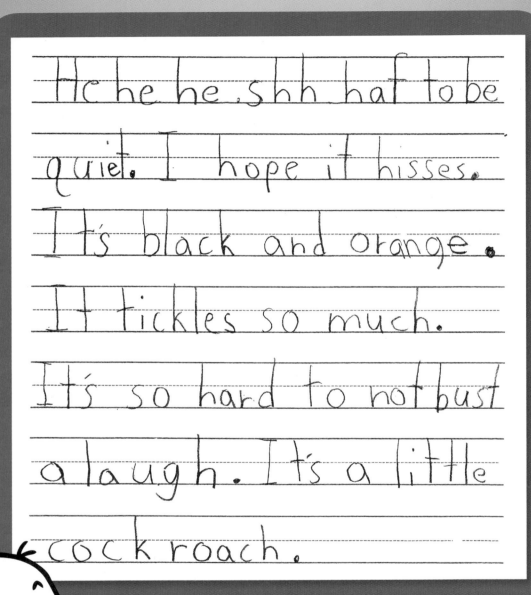

> He he he. shh haf to be quiet. I hope it hisses. It's black and orange. It tickles so much. It's so hard to not bust a laugh. It's a little cockroach.

A cockroach. Big idea or *bug* idea?

My Spelling Words

Write your five spelling words for the week here.

1. _____

2. _____

3. _____

4. _____

5. _____

Word Choice

Focus Mode: Expository

Choosing Zippy Verbs

Picking "Just Right" Words

▶ **Stretching for Never-Before-Tried Words**

Using Words to Create Meaning

Word Choice

You'll find interesting words at a museum exhibit.

You'll find them in good writing, too.

Where else can you find interesting words?

Draw and write about it on the next page.

Stretching for Never-Before-Tried Words

Where can you find interesting words?
Draw and write about it here.

A Walk in the Forest

Write facts about two or
three different kinds of trees.

I "leaf" it
to you!

Writing Sample

Mark the interesting words in this paper.

I'm a blond yellow cat. I rub up against a chair leg untill I get tunna. I look around for happynes and when I see it I purr. When I get mad I hiss like a sneaey snake.

This cat is singing my "tuna"!

Word Choice

Punctuating Powerfully

Put quotation marks around each speaker's words.

1. Trees are everywhere, the girl said.

2. She said, Trees are alive.

3. The girl asked, How do trees grow?

4. Trees grow with sunlight and water, Mom answered.

Sentence Fluency

Focus Mode: Expository

Building Complete Sentences

Starting Sentences in Different Ways

▶ **Varying Sentence Lengths**

Making Smooth-Sounding Sentences

Pants come in different lengths.

Sentences do, too.

What else comes in different lengths?

Draw and write about it on the next page.

Varying Sentence Lengths

What comes in different lengths?
Draw and write about it here.

Move Your Body!

List your favorite fitness activities in the box. Write a sentence about each activity.

I rule at jumping jacks!

Writing Sample

Write the number of words in each sentence.

Dec. 26th there was a Tsunami. over 600 people are trying to help. So far the School has collected $400.97. So maby the whole world can help. We could give them food, water, clothes, or even a home. We could mail them a letter to make them feel better. So please let's help them.

My heart is thumping!

Sentence Fluency

My Spelling Words

Write your five spelling words for the week here.

1.

2.

3.

4.

5.

Week 1 **Ideas**
Using Juicy Details

Week 2 **Organization**
Adding a Terrific Title

Week 3 **Voice**
Saying Things in New Ways

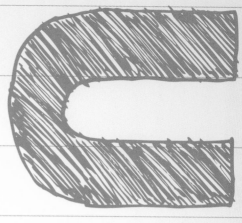

Narrative Writing Tells a Story
The writer
- tells an interesting story.
- includes characters.
- sets the story in a time and place.
- provides a problem and solution.

Ideas

Focus Mode: Narrative

Finding a Big Idea

Focusing on the Big Idea

Staying With the Big Idea

▶ **Using Juicy Details**

A painting has interesting details.

Good writing does, too.

What else has details?

Draw and write about it on the next page.

Ideas

Using Juicy Details

A good painting has interesting details. What else has details? Draw and write about it here.

Brainstorming Story Details
Plan your story. Write juicy details.

How about a talking monkey?

Who is your main character? What is his or her special power?

What does your character look like?

Does your character have a friend? What is he or she like?

When does your story take place?

Where does your story take place?

What happens in your story?

Writing Sample

Mark this paper's juicy details.

Mary is my best friend forever. She is funny and crazy and we play a lot. We are going to a play date. We are best friends for ever. Her favrtet color is blue.

My BFF makes me LOL!

Capitalizing Correctly

Circle the words that should be capitalized.

I like president Lincoln.

Is ms. Stevens your teacher?

The book is about queen Mary.

Did you see dr. Jones?

I ate lunch with principal Jackson.

Organization

Focus Mode: Narrative

Starting With a
Bold Beginning

Creating a Mighty Middle

Finishing With an
Excellent Ending

▶ **Adding a Terrific Title**

Organization

Movies have terrific titles.

Your stories should, too.

What else has a terrific title?

Draw and write about it on the next page.

Adding a Terrific Title

A movie can have a terrific title. What else has one? Draw it here. Write the title.

What Happens Next?

Plan your sequel to *Duck on a Bike.*

Goat on a boat?
Fleas on skis?

Sequel Idea

Characters

Setting

What Happens

Title Ideas

Writing Sample

**Mark the title of this piece.
What makes it terrific?**

The Flying Cookie

It was dessert time in the cafteria. When I got out my dessert I slung my bag back. The cookies flew out of my bag. One landed on the floor and a kid stepped on it. We couldnt find the other cookie unti we looked up at the window. We laughed and called it the flying cookie!

I leap for flying treats!

My Spelling Words

Write your five spelling words for the week here.

1. _____

2. _____

3. _____

4. _____

5. _____

Voice

Focus Mode: Narrative

Expressing a Feeling

Communicating With Sparkle and Pizzazz

Reaching Out to the Reader

▶ **Saying Things in New Ways**

Voice

Trying new things at the park is fun.

Trying new things in writing is, too.

What is something new you'd like to try?

Draw and write about it on the next page.

Voice

Saying Things in New Ways

What's something new you'd like to try?
Draw and write about it here.

Saying It My Way

Plan your personal narrative.

Do you think I'm an odd duck?

What new things have you tried lately?	
Details	**Say It in a New Way**
What did you do?	
How did you feel at first?	
What happened?	
How did you feel at the end?	

Writing Sample

Mark places where the writer says things in new ways.

Ch ch ch do you know
what that sound is it is sicors
cuting. Dot dot dot do you know
what that is gloo. We did a
lot of that today because we
made big bugs. befor we did that
We drew a Picher of what we
were going to make. on Tursday we
are going to make the bugs Mrs.
Voss siad.
I am going to make a Dragen
fly. Ch Ch Ch and Dot Dot
Dot!

"Quack, quack, quack..."
That's my kind of sound!

Applying Basic Grammar

Write the word that belongs in each sentence.

1. Do you _____ the answer?
   no   know

2. Kim wants to _____
   see   sea
   the movie.

3. My little brother is _____
   too   to   two
   years old.

4. Dad said _____ running!
   no   know

5. Did Mom go _____ the
   too   to   two
   store?

Week 1 **Word Choice**

Using Words to Create Meaning

Week 2 **Sentence Fluency**

Making Smooth-Sounding Sentences

Week 3 **All Traits**

Putting the Traits Together

Expository Writing Informs or Explains

The writer

• explains something interesting.

• uses facts.

• answers questions.

• focuses on what's important.

Word Choice

Focus Mode: Expository

Choosing Zippy Verbs

Picking "Just Right" Words

Stretching for Never-Before-Tried Words

▶ **Using Words to Create Meaning**

We say what we mean with signs.

We say what we mean with words, too.

How else can you say what you mean?

Draw and write about it on the next page.

Using Words to Create Meaning

What are some ways to say what you mean?
Draw and write about your idea here.

Around the House

How is a house built? List important words to know.

Parts of a House

Workers	What Workers Use

Writing Sample

Mark words that create meaning in this paper.

Dear Ms. Chase

your a wonderful teacher your like a flower bloming in sprig. and wene its raning. you give selter for a btterfly. And chiden yor btefal. And you are.

She sounds purr-fect!

Word Choice

Conventions Review

Add punctuation where it is needed
in each sentence.

1. These houses are from the past, said Miss Jan.

2. An igloo was built with blocks of ice

3. Was it warm inside

4. Wow, that cave was dark

Sentence Fluency

Focus Mode: Expository

Building Complete Sentences

Starting Sentences
in Different Ways

Varying Sentence Lengths

▶ **Making Smooth-
Sounding Sentences**

A good piece of writing sounds smooth.

Soft, sweet music does, too.

What else sounds smooth?

Draw and write about it on the next page.

Making Smooth-Sounding Sentences

What makes a smooth sound? Draw and write about it here.

Frida's Life Story

What would you like to ask Frida Kahlo about her life? Write your questions.

"Hare" I am. Start writing!

Who

What

Where

When

Writing Sample

Mark this paper's smooth-sounding sentences.

what is poetry?
poetry is moosick
to me on a pees of
paper moosick that
rimes soft moosick
to my ers.

Sentence Fluency

"Ears" to a great piece of writing!

Conventions Review

Rewrite the sentences using capital letters where they are needed.

1. We read the book frida.

2. The author is mr. jonah winter.

3. Frida was born in mexico.

4. her birthday is on july 6.

5. Mom and i like to paint, too.

- **Ideas**
- **Organization**
- **Voice**
- **Word Choice**
- **Sentence Fluency**
- **Conventions**
- **Presentation**

All Traits

Focus Mode: Expository

A puzzle has many parts that work together.

So does a great piece of writing.

What else has parts that work together?

Draw and write about it on the next page.

Putting the Traits Together

What has parts that work together?

Draw and write about it here.

My Tooth Fell Out!

Write an e-mail message telling someone what happened when you lost a tooth.

Anyone seen the Tooth Fairy?

Before My Tooth Fell Out

When My Tooth Fell Out

After My Tooth Fell Out

Writing Sample

Mark words and sentences that show good use of different traits.

My tooth fell out last night. I pulled it out my self. It still feels very wierd and it hurts. Now I can't eat on that side. I have a five dollar bill from the tooth fairy. I'm saving my money for something really cool. My dad said it wouldn't feel so raw anymore.

Chew on this story!

Conventions Review

On a separate sheet, combine the sentences in Part 1 using *and* or *but.* Rewrite the sentences in Part 2 using the correct word in parentheses.

PART 1

A tooth has a crown. A tooth has a root.

I don't like to lose teeth. I like to get money.

PART 2

Last night, the Tooth Fairy (visits, visited) me.

Mom (help, helps) me hide my tooth.

I threw my tooth into the (see, sea).

You will have (too, to, two) sets of teeth.

Week 1
Me as a Writer

Week 2
What I've Learned

Week 3
Celebrating Our Hard Work

Week 4
Cleaning Up and Having Fun

Wrapping Up the Year

Hey, writer! Aren't you proud of yourself? Your hard work as a writer has really paid off this year. Now it's time to celebrate and think about all you have learned.

Me as a Writer

What makes you special?

Every writer has something different to say. Every writer says it in his or her own way. Every writer is special.

What I Learned From

_____

- -

_____

author's name

Choose an author whose books you read this year. What did you learn about writing from him or her?

So many books, so little time.

Me as a Writer

Getting to Know Me as a Writer

What would you like next year's teacher to know about you as a writer? Write it here.

Nice to meet ya, teacha!

Letter-Writing Checklist

Write a letter to next year's teacher.

In your letter, think about including

☐ your name (My name is _____.).

☐ things you enjoy about being a writer.

☐ things that make writing hard for you.

☐ favorite topics.

☐ what helps you most.

☐ a friendly sign-off.

NOW I Know!

What have you learned about writing?

This week you'll write a paper to wrap up your writing year. It's going to be used as a celebration of everything you've learned about writing.

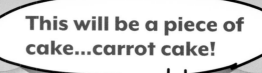

Good Writer Web

What are some things good writers do?
Use the web to help you plan your paper.

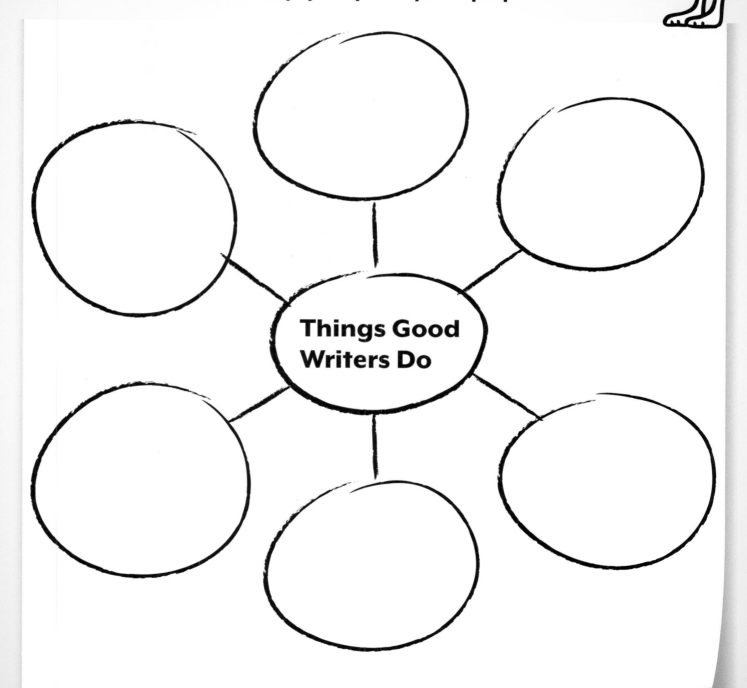

Things Good Writers Do

Trait Mates Forever!

Draw a picture of your trait mate, label it, and give a short definition.

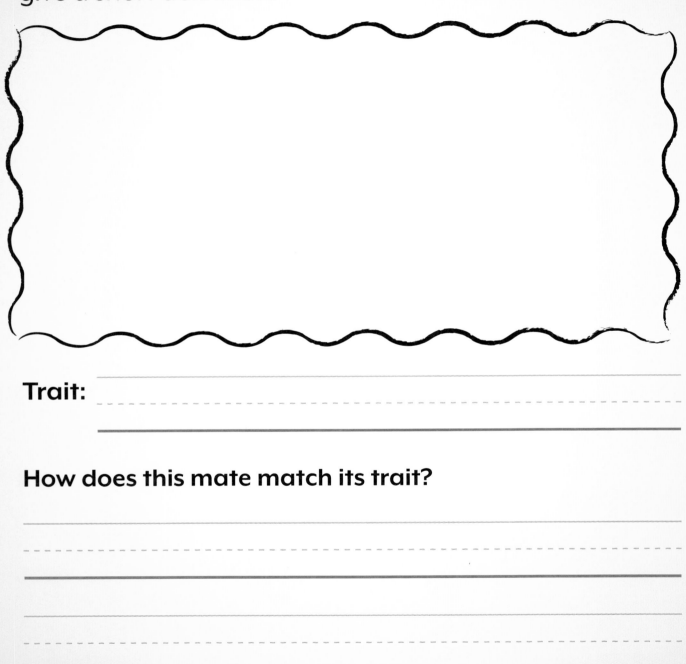

Trait: _____

How does this mate match its trait?

_____

_____

_____

Comic Strip Form

Celebrating Our Work

I am a writer.

You've had a great writing year. You've learned about everything that writers do and have written many terrific papers.

Now it's time to celebrate all that hard work. Let's have a party!

Picnic Planning List

What will we need for our picnic? Write your ideas here.

food	drinks	supplies

A picnic? Hot dog!

Organization

Celebrating Our Work

Invitation Form

You're Invited!

_____

Dear _____,

What: _____

When: _____

Where: _____

_____

_____

"I'm a Writer!" Ribbon

Make your own ribbon to celebrate your writing.

Cleaning Up and Having Fun

It's time to wrap up our year together. We'll work a little and have time for fun and games, too. It's a writing wrap!

Here's to You, _____

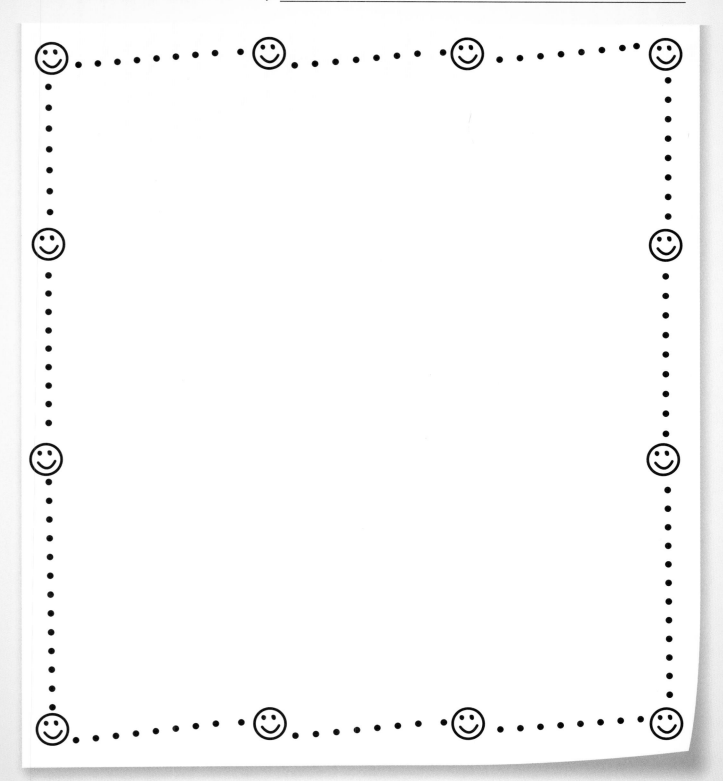

Ideas

I have a topic and I know a lot about it.

I've Got It!

On My Way

Just Beginning

Ideas

I've Got It!

- I know A LOT about this topic.
- My writing is bursting with fascinating details.
- I've picked a topic small enough to handle.

Strong

On My Way

- I know enough to get a good start.
- Some of my details are too general.
- My topic might be a little too big.

Developing

Just Beginning

- I haven't figured out what to say.
- My details aren't clear.
- I'm still thinking and looking for a topic.

Beginning

Organization

I put my ideas in an order that makes sense.

I've Got It!

On My Way

Just Beginning

Organization

Strong

I've Got It!

- I have a bold beginning, mighty middle, and excellent ending.
- My details are in the right places.
- I've given my ideas an order that really works.

Developing

On My Way

- I have a beginning, middle, and end, but they are not great.
- Most of my details fit.
- The order of my ideas makes sense.

Beginning

Just Beginning

- My writing doesn't have a clear beginning, middle, or end.
- My details are jumbled and confusing.
- I have "stuff" on paper, but it's not in order.

Voice

I made sure my writing sounds like me.

I've Got It!

On My Way

Just Beginning

Voice

Strong

I've Got It!

- My writing sounds like me.
- The reader will know I care about my topic.
- I have the right amount of energy in this piece.

Developing

On My Way

- I've played it safe. You get only a glimpse of me.
- I have only a passing interest in this topic.
- My energy level is uneven in this piece.

Beginning

Just Beginning

- I forgot to add what I think and feel in this piece.
- I really don't care about this topic.
- I'm bored and it shows.

Word Choice

I picked colorful, just-right words.

I've Got It!

On My Way

Just Beginning

Word Choice

I've Got It!

- I've picked exactly the right words.
- My words are colorful, fresh, and snappy.
- My words help the reader see my ideas.

Strong

On My Way

- Some of my words work well, but others don't.
- I've used too many ordinary words.
- My words paint only a general picture of my idea.

Developing

Just Beginning

- I'm confused about how to use words well.
- I've left out key words.
- I've used the wrong word or used the same word over and over.

Beginning

Sentence Fluency

I wrote sentences that sound great.

I've Got It!

On My Way

Just Beginning

Sentence Fluency

Strong

I've Got It!

- My sentences are well built and easy to read aloud.
- The way my sentences begin makes them interesting.
- I've varied my sentence lengths.

Developing

On My Way

- I've got sentences! Some of them are hard to read aloud, though.
- I tried a couple of different ways to begin my sentences.
- I could combine some of my sentences or cut a few apart.

Beginning

Just Beginning

- I am having trouble making a sentence.
- My beginnings all sound the same.
- I've used *and* too many times, or many sentences are too short.

Conventions

I cleaned up my writing for my reader.

I've Got It!

On My Way

Just Beginning

Conventions

Strong

I've Got It!

- My spelling is magnificent.
- All my capitals are in the right place.
- I used punctuation correctly.
- My grammar is great.
- I've done a great job proofreading.

Developing

On My Way

- I've spelled simple words correctly.
- I've used capitals in easy spots.
- My punctuation is correct in some places, but not in others.
- I've proofread quickly and missed things.

Beginning

Just Beginning

- My writing is hard to read because of my spelling.
- My capitals don't follow the rules.
- I haven't used punctuation well at all.
- I forgot to proofread.

Presentation

I dressed up my writing so it's ready to share.

I've Got It!

On My Way

Just Beginning

Presentation

Strong

I've Got It!

- My paper is neat—no smudges or cross-outs.
- My letters are neatly formed.
- I have margins that make a frame.

Developing

On My Way

- My paper can be read, but it's not my best.
- Some of my letters are neatly formed, but some are not.
- My margins work better in some places than in others.

Beginning

Just Beginning

- My paper is very hard to read.
- My letters are a mess.
- I forgot to use margins.

The Writing Song

(sung to the tune of "It's Raining, It's Pouring")

I'm writing, I'm writing.

The whole world is cheering.

I write for you,

and I write for me.

And every day—I'm improving!

The Spelling Song

(sung to the tune of "Ta-ra-ra Boom-de-ay")

These are my spelling words.

I use them every day.

I write them carefully

because I know the way!

[Recite the week's five spelling words.]

These are my spelling words.

I use them every day.

If I don't spell them right,

I'll learn them right away. Hey!

The Ideas Song

(sung to the tune of "Row, Row, Row Your Boat")

Write, write, write your thoughts.

Make your ideas clear.

Tell the reader what you know

And what you hold most dear.

The Organization Song

(sung to the tune of "Pop Goes the Weasel")

A good beginning, middle, and end help to shape your writing.

Placing details where they make sense—

Pop! It's inviting.

You start it off with something fine.

Next comes something exciting.

Your perfect ending wraps it up.

Bam! Now you're writing.

The Voice Song

(sung to the tune of "If You're Happy and You Know It")

If you're happy and you know it, that's your voice.

If you're thoughtful and you know it, that's your voice.

If you're spunky and you know it,

then your words will surely show it.

If you're happy and you know it, that's your voice.

The Word Choice Song

(sung to the tune of "Ring Around the Rosie")

Writing with your

best words—

Finding lots of

new words—

Sparkle! Dazzle!

The words stand out.

The Sentence Fluency Song

(sung to the tune of "Frère Jacques")

Sentence fluency,

Sentence fluency.

The writing flows.

The writing flows.

Sentences are longer.

Sentences are shorter.

It sounds smooth;

It sounds right.

The Conventions Song

(sung to the tune of "The Hokey Pokey")

You put your periods in.

You check your spelling out.

You put your capitals in.

And you shake them all about.

You make your paper better

when you edit it just right.

That's what it's all about.

The Presentation Song

(sung to the tune of "Yankee Doodle")

Take a look at what you wrote.

Does it look nice and neat?

Have you done the best you could

so reading is a treat?

Have you written carefully?

Is your writing clear?

Not a single cross-out, smudge

will you or I find there.

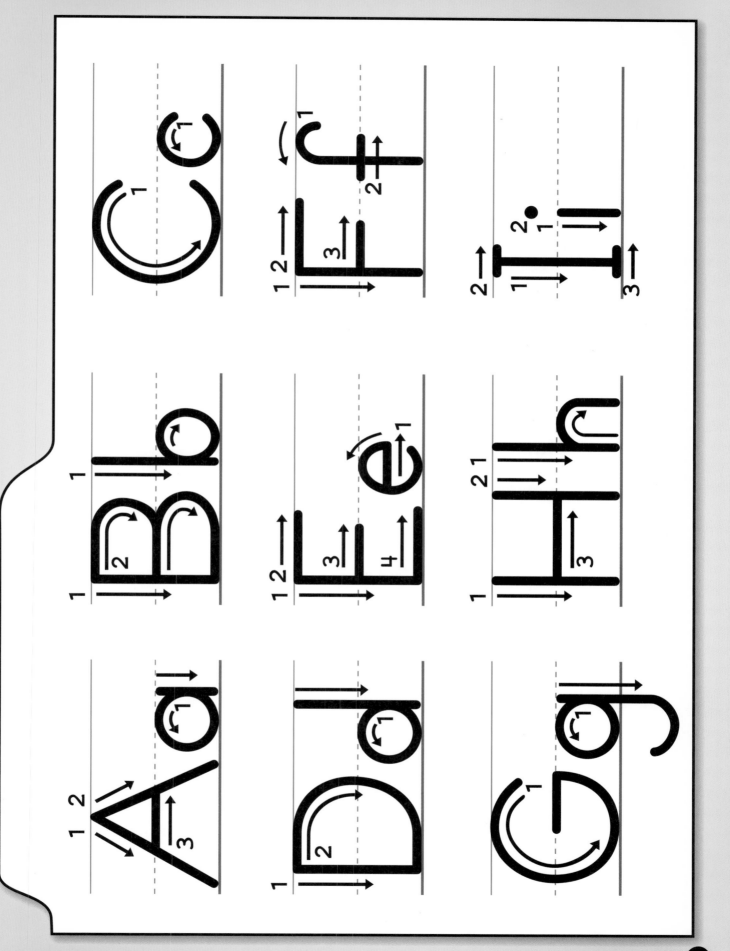

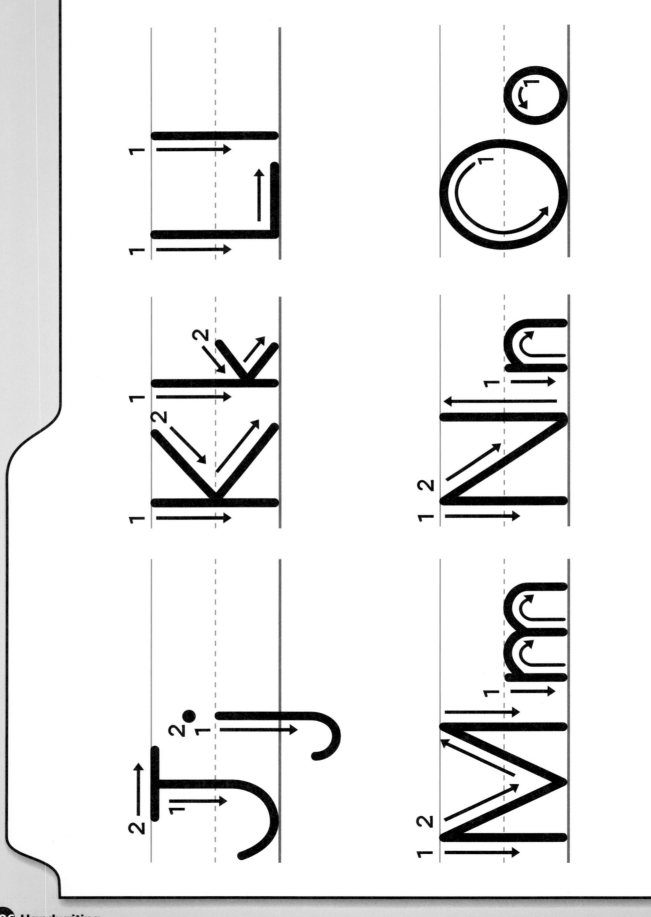

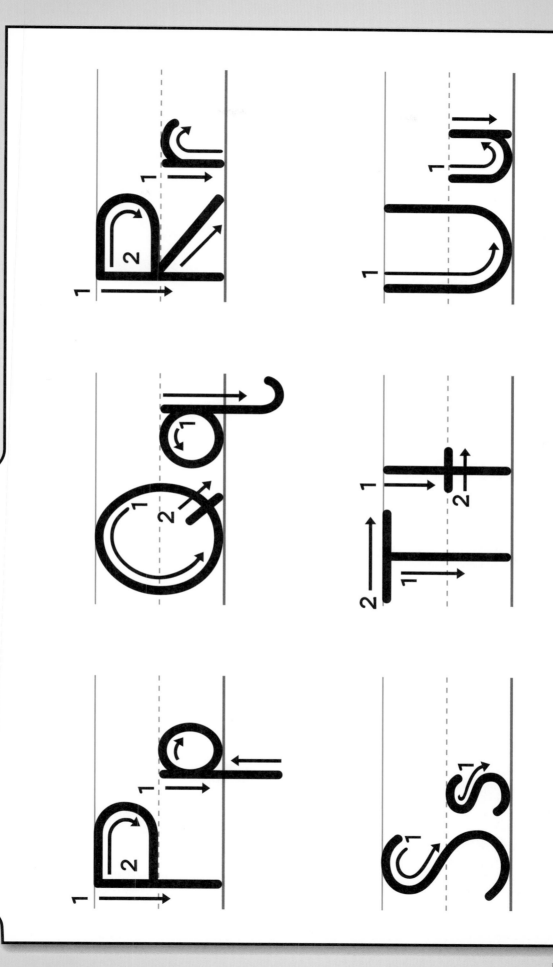